Dear Reader,

The holiday season is [...] year and all of us at t[...] would like to extend [...] you and your loved on[...]

To help you celebrate, our editors have chosen *Let It Snow* as our special gift to you. This is a story of two people, stranded in a blizzard at Christmas, who find in each other the greatest Christmas gift of all, love.

We hope you'll enjoy Shelly and Slade's story, and we hope you have the happiest of holidays.

Pam Powers

Debbie Macomber

Let It Snow

Harlequin Books

ISBN: 0-373-15187-X

Chapter One

"Ladies and gentlemen, this is your captain speaking."

Shelly Griffin's fingers compressed around the armrest until her neatly manicured nails threatened to cut into the fabric of the airplane seat. Flying had never thrilled her, and she avoided planes whenever possible. It had taken her the better part of a month to convince herself that she'd be perfectly safe. She told herself that the Boeing 727 would take off without incident from San Francisco and land unscathed ninety minutes later in Seattle. Flying, after all, was said to be relatively riskless. But if it wasn't Christmas, if she wasn't so homesick and if she'd had more than four days off, she would have done anything to get home for the holidays—except fly.

"Seattle reports heavy snow and limited visibility," the captain continued. "We've been rerouted to Portland International until the Seattle runways can be cleared."

A low groan filled the plane.

Shelly relaxed. Snow. She could handle snow. She wasn't overjoyed with the prospect of having to land twice, but she was so close to home now that she would have willingly suffered anything to see a welcoming smile light up her father's eyes.

In an effort to divert her thoughts away from impending tragedy, Shelly studied the passengers around her. A grandmotherly type slept sedately in the seat beside her. The man sitting across the aisle was such a classic businessman that he was intriguing. Almost from the moment they'd left San Francisco, he'd been working out of his briefcase. He hadn't so much as cracked a smile during the entire flight. The captain's announcement had produced little more than a disgruntled flicker in his staid exterior.

Shelly had seen enough men like him in her job as a reporter in the federal court to catalog him quickly. Polished. Professional. Impeccable. Handsome, too, Shelly supposed, if she was interested, which she wasn't. She preferred her men a little less intense. She managed to suppress a tight laugh. Men! What men? In the ten months she'd been living in the City by the Bay, she hadn't exactly developed a following. A few interesting prospects now and again but nothing serious.

As the Boeing 727 slowly made its descent, Shelly's fingers gripped the armrest with renewed tension. Her gaze skimmed the emergency exits as she reviewed affirmations on the safety of flying. She mumbled them under her breath as the plane angled sharply to the right, aligning its giant bulk with the narrow runway ahead.

Keeping her eyes centered on the seat in front of her, Shelly held her breath until she felt the wheels gently bounce against the runway in a flawless landing. A burst of noise accompanied the aircraft as it slowed to a crawl.

The oxygen rushed from Shelly's lungs in a heart-felt sigh of relief. Somehow the landings were so much worse than the takeoffs. As the tension eased from her rigid body, she looked around to discover the businessman slanting his idle gaze over her. His dark eyes contained a look of surprise. He seemed amazed that anyone could be afraid of flying, and he was utterly indifferent to her apprehension. The blood mounted briefly in her pale features, and Shelly decided she definitely didn't like this cheerless executive.

The elderly woman sitting next to her placed a hand on Shelly's forearm. "Are you all right, dear?"

"Of course." Relief throbbed in her voice. Now that they were on the ground, she could feign the composure that seemed to come so easily to the other passengers.

"I hope we aren't delayed long. My daughter's taking off work to meet my flight."

"My dad's forty minutes from the airport," Shelly murmured, hoping that he'd called the airline to check if her flight was on time. She hated the thought of him anxiously waiting for her.

The other woman craned her neck to peek out the small side window. "It doesn't seem to be snowing much here. Just a few flakes floating down like lazy goose feathers."

Shelly grinned at the verbal picture. "Let's hope it stays that way."

She remained seated while several of the other passengers got up and left the plane. The businessman was among those who quickly vacated their seats. From what the captain had said, they wouldn't be in

Portland long, and Shelly didn't want to take a chance of missing the flight.

After checking her watch every ten minutes for forty minutes, Shelly was convinced that they'd never leave Oregon. The blizzard had hit the area, and whirling snow buffeted the quiet plane with growing intensity. Her anxieties mounted with equal force.

"This is the captain speaking." His faint Southern drawl filled the plane. "Unfortunately, Seattle reports that visibility hasn't improved. They're asking that we remain here in Portland for another half hour, possibly longer."

Frustration and disappointment erupted from the passengers seated on the plane, and they all began speaking at once.

"This is the captain again," the pilot added, his low drawl riddled with wry humor. "I'd like to remind those of you who are upset by our situation that it's far better to be on the ground wishing you were in the sky than to be in the sky *praying* you were on the ground."

Shelly added a silent amen to that! As it was, she was beginning to feel claustrophobic trapped inside the plane. Unsnapping her seat belt, she stood, reached for her purse and headed down the narrow aisle toward the front of the plane.

"Do I have time to make a phone call?"

"Sure," the flight attendant answered with a cordial smile. "Don't be long, though. The conditions in Seattle could change quickly."

"I won't," Shelly promised and made her way into the airport terminal.

It wasn't until she was sorting through her purse for change that she noted the unsympathetic businessman from her flight had the phone booth adjacent to hers.

"This is Slade Garner again," he announced with the faintest trace of impatience creeping into his voice. "My plane's still in Portland."

A pause followed while Shelly dumped the contents of her coin purse into her hand and scowled. She didn't have change for the phone.

"Yes, yes, I understand the snow's a problem on your end as well," he continued smoothly. "I doubt that I'll make it in this afternoon. Perhaps we should arrange the meeting for first thing tomorrow morning. Nine o'clock?" Another pause. "Of course I realize it's the day before Christmas."

Rummaging in her purse for a quarter, Shelly managed to dredge up a token for the cable car, a dried peach pit and a lost button.

Pressing her lips tightly together, she mused what a coldhearted tycoon this businessman had to be to insist upon a meeting so close to Christmas. Instantly she felt guilty because her thoughts were so judgmental. Of course he'd want to keep his appointment. He certainly hadn't taken this flight for his health. Her second regret was that she had intentionally eavesdropped on his conversation, looking for excuses to justify her dislike of him. Such behavior was hardly in keeping with the Christmas spirit.

Pasting on a pleasant smile, Shelly stepped forward when Slade Garner replaced the receiver. Abruptly he turned around.

"Excuse me." His gaze refused to meet hers, and for a second Shelly didn't think that he'd heard her.

"Yes?" His expression was bored, frustrated.

"Have you got change for a dollar?" She unfolded a crisp one-dollar bill, anticipating the exchange.

Slade uninterestedly checked the contents of his pocket, glaring down at the few coins in his palm. "Sorry." Dispassionately he tucked them back in his pocket and turned away from her.

Shelly was ready to approach someone else when Slade turned back to her. His dark brows drew together in a frown as something about her registered in his preoccupied thoughts. "You were on the Seattle flight?"

"Yes."

"Here." He handed her a quarter.

The corners of Shelly's mouth curved up in surprise. "Thanks." She was convinced that he hadn't heard her as he briskly walked away. Shelly didn't know what difference it made that they'd shared the same plane. Without analyzing his generosity any further, she dropped the coin in the slot.

After connecting with the operator, Shelly shifted her weight from one foot to the other while the phone rang, waiting for her father to answer.

"Dad."

"Merry Christmas, Shortcake."

Her father had bestowed this affectionate title on Shelly when she was a young teen and her friends had sprouted around her. To her dismay Shelly had remained a deplorable five foot until she was seventeen. Then within six months she had grown five inches. Her height and other attributes of puberty had been hormonal afterthoughts.

"I'm in Portland."

"I know. When I phoned Sea-Tac, the lady at the reservation desk told me you'd been forced to land there. How are you doing?"

"Fine." She fibbed about her dread of flying. "I'm sorry about the delay."

"That's not your fault."

"But I hate wasting precious hours sitting here when I could be with you."

"Don't worry about it. We'll have plenty of time together."

"Have you decorated the tree yet?" Since her mother's death three years before, Shelly and her father had made a ritual of placing the homemade ornaments on the tree together.

"I haven't even bought one. I thought we'd do that first thing in the morning."

Shelly closed her eyes, savoring the warmth of love and security that the sound of her father's voice always gave her. "I've got a fantastic surprise for you."

"What's that?" her father prompted.

"It wouldn't be a surprise if I told you, would it?"

Her father chuckled and Shelly could visualize him rubbing his finger over his upper lip the way he did when something amused him.

"I've missed you, Dad."

"I know. I've missed you, too."

"Take care."

"I will." She was about to hang up. "Dad," she added hastily, her thoughts churning as her gaze focused on a huge wall advertisement for a rental car agency. "Listen, don't go the the airport until I phone."

"But—"

"By the time you arrive, I'll have collected my things and be waiting outside for you. That way you won't have to park."

"I don't mind, Shortcake."

"I know, but it'll work better this way."

"If you insist."

"I do." Her brothers claimed that their father was partial to his only daughter. It was a long-standing family joke that she was the only one capable of swaying him once he'd made a decision. "I do insist."

They said their goodbyes, and after Shelly disconnected the line, she checked for the quarter that had slipped into the change slot. Feeling light-hearted and relieved, she flipped it in the air with a flick of her thumb and caught it with a dexterity that surprised her. Instead of heading down the concourse toward the plane, she ventured in the opposite direction, taking the escalators to the lower level and the rental car agencies.

To her surprise Shelly found that she wasn't the only one with alternate transportation in mind. The businessman who had loaned her the quarter was talking with a young man at the first agency. Shelly walked past him to the second counter.

"How much would it cost to rent a car here and drop it off in Seattle?" she asked brightly.

The tall, college-aged woman hardly looked up from the computer screen. "Sorry, we don't have any cars available."

"None?" Shelly found that hard to believe.

"Lots of people have had the same idea as you," the clerk explained. "A plane hasn't landed in Seattle in hours. No one wants to sit around the airport waiting. Especially at Christmas."

"Thanks, anyway." Shelly scooted down to the third agency and repeated her question.

"Yes, we do," the clerk said with a wide grin. "We only have one car available at the moment." She named a sum that caused Shelly to swallow heavily. But already the idea had gained momentum in her mind. Every minute the plane remained on the ground robbed her of precious time with her father. And from what he'd told her, the snow was coming down fast and furiously. It could be hours before the plane was able to take off. She freely admitted that another landing at another airport in the middle of the worst snowstorm of the year wasn't her idea of a good time. As it was, her Christmas bonus was burning a hole in her purse. It was a good cause. Surely there was some unwritten rule that stated every favorite daughter should spend Christmas with her father.

"If she doesn't take the car, I will." Slade Garner spoke from beside Shelly. A wide, confident smile spread across his handsome features.

"I want it," she cried. His aura of self-assurance bordered on arrogance.

"I have to get to Seattle."

"So do I!" she informed him primly. In case he mentioned that he'd loaned her the quarter, she pulled it from her jacket pocket and handed it to him.

"I've got an important meeting."

"As a matter of fact, so do I." Turning back to the counter, Shelly picked up a pen and prepared to fill in the rental form.

"How much?" Slade asked. His features tightened with unrelenting resolve that negated his manly appeal.

"I beg your pardon?"

"How much do you want for the car?" His hand slipped into the pocket of his suit coat, apparently prepared to pay her price.

Squaring her shoulders with angry frustration, Shelly exchanged looks with the clerk. "Get your own car."

"There's only one car available. This one."

"And I've got it," she told him with a deceptively calm smile. The more she saw of this man, the more aggravating he became.

His jaw tightened. "I don't think you understand," he said and breathed out with sharp impatience. "My meeting's extremely important."

"So is mine. I'm—"

"You could share the car," the clerk suggested, causing both Shelly and Slade to divert their shocked gazes to the impromptu peacemaker.

Shelly hesitated.

Slade's brows arched. "I'll pay the full fee for the car," he offered.

"You mention money one more time and the deal's off," she shot back hotly.

"Don't be unreasonable."

"I'm not being unreasonable. You are."

Slade rubbed a hand along the back of his neck and forcefully expelled his breath. "Have we or have we not got a deal?"

"I'm not going to Seattle."

He gave her a sharp look of reproach. "I just heard you say Seattle."

"I'm headed for Maple Valley. That's in south King County."

"Fine. I'll drop you off and deliver the car to the rental place myself."

That would save her one hassle. Still, she hesitated. Two minutes together and they were already arguing. Shelly wondered how they'd possibly manage three hours cooped up in the close confines of a car.

"Listen," he argued, his voice tinged with exasperation. "If I make it into Seattle this afternoon, I might be able to get this meeting over with early. That way I can be back in San Francisco for Christmas."

Quickly he'd discerned the weakest link in her chain of defenses and had aimed there. Christmas and home were important to her.

"All right," she mumbled. "But I'll pay my share of the fee."

"Whatever you want, lady."

For the first time since she'd seen him, Slade Garner smiled.

Chapter Two

"What about your luggage?" Slade asked as they strolled down the concourse toward the plane.

"I only have one bag. It's above my seat." Honey-brown hair curled around her neck, and she absently lifted a strand and looped it over her ear. A farm girl's wardrobe didn't fit in with the formal business attire she needed in San Francisco so Shelly had left most of her clothes with her father. Now she realized that having packed light was a blessing in disguise. At least there wouldn't be the hassle of trying to get her suitcase back.

Shelly's spirits buoyed up; she was heading home and she wasn't flying!

"Good. I only have a garment bag with me."

Shelly hesitated. "I have another bag filled with presents."

Slade's gaze briefly scanned hers. "That shouldn't be any problem."

When he sees the monstrosity, he might change his mind, Shelly mused good-naturedly. In addition to a variety of odd-sized gifts, she had brought her father several long loaves of sourdough bread. The huge package was awkward, and Shelly had required the flight attendant's assistance to place it in the compartment above her seat. Normally Shelly would have checked a bundle that size with the airline. But with the long loaves of bread sticking out like doughy antennas, that had been impossible.

The plane was nearly empty when they boarded, confirming her suspicion that the delay was going to be far longer than originally anticipated. Checking her watch, she discovered that it was nearly noon. The other passengers had probably gone to get something to eat.

Standing on the cushioned seat beside hers, Shelly opened the storage compartment.

"Do you need help?" Slade asked. A dark gray garment bag was folded neatly over his forearm.

"Here." Shelly handed him her one small bag. She heard him mumble something about appreciating a woman who packed light and smiled to herself.

Straining to stretch as far as she could to get a good grip on her package, she heard Slade grumble.

"Look at what some idiot put up there."

"Pardon?"

"That bag. Good grief, people should know better than to try to force a tuba case up there."

"That's mine and it isn't a tuba case." Extracting the bag containing the bread, she handed it down to him.

Slade looked at it as if something were about to leap out and bite him. "Good heavens, what is this?"

What is it! Bread had to be the most recognizable item in the world. And to have it shaped in long, thin loaves wasn't that unusual, either!

"A suitcase for a snake," she replied sarcastically.

The beginnings of a grin touched his usually impassive features as he gently moved in front of her. "Let me get that thing down before you fall."

Shelly climbed down from the cushioned seat. "Suitcase for a snake, huh?" Unexpectedly Slade Garner smiled, and the effect on Shelly was dazzling. She had the feeling that this man didn't often take the time to laugh and enjoy life. Only minutes before she'd classified him as cheerless and intense. But when he smiled, the carefully guarded facade cracked and she was given a rare glimpse of the intriguing man inside. And he fascinated her.

By the time they'd cleared their tickets with the airline, the courtesy car from the rental agency had arrived to deliver them to their rented vehicle.

"I put everything in my name," Slade said on a serious note. The snow continued to fall, creating a picturesque view.

"That's fine." He'd taken the small suitcase from her, leaving her to cope with the huge sack filled with Christmas goodies.

"It means I'll be doing all the driving."

One glance at the snowstorm and Shelly was grateful.

"Well?" He looked as though he expected an argument.

"Do you have a driver's license?"

Again a grin cracked the tight line of his mouth, touching his eyes. "Yes."

"Then there shouldn't be any problem."

He paused, looking down on her. "Are you always so witty?"

Shelly chuckled, experiencing a rush of pleasure at her ability to make him smile. "Only when I try to be. Come on, Garner, loosen up. It's Christmas."

"I've got a meeting to attend. Just because it happens to fall close to a holiday doesn't make a whit's difference."

"Yeah, but just think, once you're through, you can hurry home and spend the holidays with your family."

"Right." The jagged edge of his clipped reply was revealing, causing Shelly to wonder if he had a family.

As they deposited their luggage in the trunk of the rented Camaro, Shelly had the opportunity to study Slade. The proud, withdrawn look revealed little of his thoughts; there was an air of independence about him. Even with a minimum of contact, she realized that he must possess a keen and agile mind. He was a man of contrasts—pensive yet decisive, cultured while maintaining a highly organized facade.

Standing in the fallen snow, the young man at the rental agency handed Slade a map of the city and pointed him in the direction of the nearest freeway entrance ramp.

After studying the map thoroughly, Slade handed it to Shelly. "Are you ready?"

"Forward, James," she teased, climbing into the passenger seat and rubbing her bare hands together to generate some warmth. When she'd left San Francisco that morning, she hadn't dressed for snow.

With a turn of the key, Slade started the engine and adjusted the heater. "You'll be warm in a minute."

Shelly nodded, burying her hands in her jacket pockets. "You know, if it gets much colder, we might get snow before we reach Seattle."

"Very funny," he muttered dryly, snapping his seat belt into place. Hands gripping the wheel, Slade hesitated. "Do you want to find a phone and call your husband?"

"I'm visiting my dad," she corrected. "I'm not married. And no. If I told him what we're doing, he'd only worry."

Slade shifted gears and they pulled onto the road.

"Do you want to contact . . . your wife?"

"I'm not married."

"Oh." Shelly prayed that the small expression wouldn't reveal her satisfaction at the information. It wasn't often that she found herself so fascinated by a man. The crazy part was that she wasn't entirely sure she liked him, but he attracted her.

"I'm engaged," he added.

"Oh." She swallowed convulsively. So much for that. "When's the wedding?"

The windshield wipers hummed ominously. "In approximately two years."

Shelly nearly choked in an effort to hide her shock.

"Both Margaret and I have professional and financial goals we hope to accomplish before we marry." He drove with his back stiff, his expression sullen. "Margaret feels we should save fifty thousand dollars before we think about marriage and I agree. We both have strong feelings about having a firm financial foundation."

"I can't imagine waiting two years to marry the man I loved."

"But then you're entirely different from Margaret."

As far as Shelly was concerned, that was the nicest thing anyone had said to her all day. "We do agree on one thing, though. I feel a marriage should last forever." But for Shelly love had to be more spontaneous and far less calculated. "My parents had a marvelous marriage," she said, filling the silence. "I only hope that, when I marry, my own will be as happy." She went on to elaborate how her parents had met one Christmas and were married two months later on Valentine's Day. Their marriage, Shelly told him complacently, had been blessed with love and happiness for nearly twenty-seven years before her mother's unexpected death. It took great restraint not to mention that her parents had barely had twenty dollars between them when they'd taken their vows. At the time her father had been a student of veterinary medicine with only two years of schooling behind him. They'd managed without a huge bank balance.

From the tight lines around his mouth and nose, Shelly could tell that Slade found the whole story trite.

"Is your sweet tale of romance supposed to touch my heart?"

Furious, Shelly straightened and looked out the side window at the snow-covered trees that lined the side of Interstate 5. "No. I was just trying to find out if you had one."

"Karate mouth strikes again," he mumbled.

"Karate mouth?" Shelly was too stunned at Slade's unexpected display of wit to do anything more than repeat his statement.

"You have the quickest comeback of anyone I know." Admiration flashed unchecked in his gaze before he turned his attention back to the freeway.

Shelly was more interested in learning about Margaret so she tried to keep the conversation away from herself. "I imagine you're anxious to get back to spend Christmas with Margaret." She regretted her earlier judgmental attitude toward Slade. He had good reason for wanting this meeting over.

"Margaret's visiting an aunt in Arizona during the holidays. She left a couple of days ago."

"So you won't be together." The more she heard of Margaret, the more curious Shelly became about a woman who would agree to wait two years for marriage. "Did she give you your Christmas gift before she left?" The type of gift one gave was always telling.

Slade hesitated. "Margaret and I agreed to forgo giving gifts this year."

Shelly had barely managed to control her tongue when he had spouted off about his long engagement, but this was too much. "Not exchange gifts? That's terrible."

"We have financial goals," Slade growled irritably. "Wasting money on trivialities simply deters us from our two-year plan. Christmas gifts aren't going to advance our desires."

At the moment Shelly sincerely doubted that good ol' Margaret and Slade had "desires."

"I bet Margaret's just saying she doesn't want a gift," Shelly offered. "She's probably secretly hoping you'll break down and buy her something. It doesn't have to be something big. Any woman appreciates roses."

Her companion gave an expressive shrug. "I thought flowers would be a nice touch myself, but Margaret claims they make her sneeze. Besides, roses at Christmas are terribly expensive. A waste of money, really."

"Naturally," Shelly muttered under her breath. She was beginning to get a clearer picture of this stuffy fellow and his ever-so-practical fiancée.

"Did you say something?" A hint of challenge echoed in his cool tones.

"Not really." Leaning forward, she fiddled with the radio dial, trying to find a station that was playing music. "What's Margaret do, by the way?"

"She's a systems analyst."

Shelly arched both eyebrows in mute comment. This was the type of occupation that she expected from a nuts-and-bolts person like Margaret. "What about children?"

"What about them?"

Shelly realized that she was prying, but she couldn't help herself. "Are you planning a family?"

"Of course. We're hoping that Margaret can schedule a leave of absence in eight years."

"You'll be near forty!" The exclamation burst from her lips before Shelly could hold it back.

"Forty-one, actually. Do you disapprove of that, too?"

Shelly swallowed uncomfortably and paid an inordinate amount of attention to the radio, not understanding why she couldn't get any music. "I apologize, I didn't mean to sound so judgmental. It's just that—"

"It's just that you've never been goal oriented."

"But I have," she argued. "I've always wanted to be a court reporter. It's a fascinating job."

"I imagine that you're good at anything you put your mind to."

The unexpected compliment caught her completely off guard. "What a nice thing to say."

"If you put your mind to it, you might figure out why you can't get the radio working."

Her gaze flickered automatically from Slade to the dial. Before she could comment, he reached over and twisted a knob. "It's a bit difficult to pick up the transmission waves when the radio isn't turned on."

"Right." She'd been too preoccupied with asking about Margaret to notice. Color flooded into her cheeks at her own stupidity. Slade flustered her and that hadn't happened in a long time. She had the feeling that, in a battle of words, he would parry her barbs as expertly as a professional swordsman.

Soft, soothing music filled the car. Warm and snug, Shelly leaned back against the headrest and cushioned seat and hummed along, gazing at the flakes of falling snow.

"With the snow and all it really feels like Christmas," she murmured, fearing more questions would destroy the tranquil mood.

"It's caused nothing but problems."

"I suppose, but it's so lovely."

"Of course it's lovely. You're sitting in a warm chauffeur-driven car with the radio playing."

"Grumble, grumble, grumble," she tossed back lightly. "Bah, humbug!"

"Bah, humbug," he echoed, and to her astonishment Slade laughed. The sound of it was rich and full and caused Shelly to laugh with him. When the radio played a Bing Crosby Christmas favorite, Shelly sang along. Soon Slade's deep baritone joined her clear soprano in sweet harmony. The lyrics spoke of dreaming, and Shelly's mind conjured up her own longings. She was comfortable with this man when she'd expected to find a dozen reasons to dislike him. Instead, she discovered that she was attracted to someone who was engaged to another woman. A man who was intensely loyal. This was the usual way her life ran. She was attracted to Slade, but she didn't know where this feeling would lead. She wasn't entirely sure that her insights about him were on base. As uncharitable as it sounded, she may have formed these feelings simply because she considered him too good for someone like Margaret.

Disgusted with herself, Shelly closed her eyes and rested her head against the window. The only sounds were the soft melodies playing on the radio and the discordant swish of the windshield wipers. Occasionally a gust of wind would cause the car to veer slightly.

A gentle hand on her shoulder shook her. "Shelly."

With a start she bolted upright. "What's wrong?"

Slade had pulled over to the shoulder of the freeway. The snow was so thick that Shelly couldn't see two feet in front of her.

"I don't think we can go any further," Slade announced.

Chapter Three

"We can't stay here," Shelly cried, looking at their precarious position beside the road. Snow whirled in every direction. The ferocity of the storm shocked her, whipping and howling around them. She found it little short of amazing that Slade had been able to steer the car at all. While she'd slept, the storm had worsened drastically.

"Do you have any other suggestions?" he said and breathed out sharply.

He was angry, but his irritation wasn't directed at her. Wearily she lifted the hair from her smooth brow. "No, I guess I don't."

Silence seeped around them as Slade turned off the car's engine. Gone was the soothing sound of Christmas music, the hum of the engine and the rhythmic swish of the windshield wipers. Together they sat waiting for the fury to lessen so that they could start up again. Staring out at the surrounding area between bursts of wind and snow, Shelly guessed that they weren't far from Castle Rock and Mount St. Helens.

After ten minutes of uneasiness, she decided to be the first to break the gloom. "Are you hungry?" She stared at the passive, unyielding face beside her.

"No."

"I am."

"Have some of that bread." He cocked his head toward the back seat where she'd stuck the huge loaves of sourdough bread.

"I couldn't eat Dad's bread. He'd never forgive me."

"He'd never forgive you if you starved to death, either."

Glancing down at her pudgy thighs, Shelly sadly shook her head. "There's hardly any chance of that."

"What makes you say that? You're not fat. In fact, I'd say you were just about perfect."

"Me? Perfect?" A burst of embarrassed laughter slid from her throat. Reaching for her purse, she removed her wallet.

"What are you doing?"

"I'm going to pay you for saying that."

Slade chuckled. "What makes you think you're overweight?"

"You mean aside from the fat all over my body?"

"I'm serious."

She shrugged. "I don't know. I just feel chubby. Since leaving home, I don't get enough exercise. I couldn't very well bring Sampson with me."

"Sampson?"

"My horse. I used to ride him every day."

"If you've gained any weight, it's in all the right places."

His gaze fell to her lips, and Shelly's senses churned in quivering awareness. He stared into her dark eyes and blinked as if not believing what he saw. For her part, Shelly studied him with open curiosity. His eyes were smoky dark, his face blunt and sensual. His brow was creased as though he was giving the moment grave consideration. Thick eyebrows arched heavily over his eyes.

Abruptly he pulled his gaze away and leaned forward to start the engine. The accumulated snow on the windshield was brushed aside with a flip of the wiper switch. "Isn't that a McDonald's up ahead?"

Shelly squinted to catch a glimpse of the world-famous golden arches. "Hey, I think it is."

"The exit can't be far."

"Do you think we can make it?"

"I think we'd better," he mumbled.

Shelly understood. The car had become their private cocoon, unexpectedly intimate and highly sensual. Under normal circumstances they wouldn't have given each other more than a passing glance. What was happening wasn't magic but something far more exhilarating.

With the wipers beating furiously against the window, Slade inched the car to the exit, which proved to be less than a half mile away.

Slowly they crawled down the side road that paralleled the freeway. With some difficulty Slade was able to find a place to park in the restaurant's lot. Shelly sighed with relief. This was the worst storm she could remember. Wrapping her coat securely around her, she reached for her purse.

"You ready?" she blurted out, opening the car door.

"Anytime."

Hurriedly Slade joined her and tightly grasped her elbow as they stepped together toward the front entrance of the fast-food restaurant. Pausing just inside the door to stamp the snow from their shoes, they glanced up to note that several other travelers were stranded there as well.

They ordered hamburgers and coffee and sat down by the window.

"How long do you think we'll be here?" Shelly asked, not really expecting an answer. She needed reassurance more than anything. This Christmas holiday hadn't started out on the right foot. But of one thing she was confident—the plane hadn't left Portland yet.

"Your guess is as good as mine."

"I'd say two hours, then," she murmured, taking a bite of her Big Mac.

"Why two hours?"

"I don't know. It sounds reasonable. If it's longer than that, I might start to panic. But, if worse comes to worst, I can think of less desirable places to spend Christmas. At least we won't starve."

Slade muttered something unintelligible under his breath and continued eating. When he finished, he excused himself and returned to the car for his briefcase.

Shelly bought two more cups of coffee and propped her feet on the seat opposite her. Taking the latest issue of *Mad Magazine* from her purse, she was absorbed in it by the time he returned. Her gaze dared him to comment on her reading material. Her reading *Mad Magazine* was a long-standing joke between

Shelly and her father. He expected it of her and read each issue himself so that he could tease her about the contents. Since moving, she'd fallen behind by several months and wanted to be prepared when she saw her dad again. She didn't expect Slade to understand her tastes.

He rejoined her and gave her little more than a conciliatory glance before reclaiming his seat and briskly opening the *Wall Street Journal*.

Their reading choices said a lot about each other, Shelly realized. Rarely had she seen two people less alike. A lump grew in her throat. She liked Slade. He was the type of man she'd willingly give up *Mad Magazine* for.

An hour later a contented Shelly set the December issue aside and reached in her purse for the romance novel that she kept tucked away. It wasn't often that she was so at ease with a man. She didn't feel the overwhelming urge to keep a conversation going or fill the silence with chatter. They were comfortable together.

Without a word she went to the counter and bought a large order of fries and placed them in the middle of the table. Now and then, her eyes never leaving the printed page, she blindly reached for a fry. Once her groping hand bumped another, and her startled gaze collided with Slade's.

"Sorry," he muttered.

"Don't be. They're for us both."

"They get to be addictive, don't they?"

"Sort of like reading the *Wall Street Journal*?"

"I wondered if you'd comment on that."

Shelly laughed. "I was expecting you to mention my choice."

"*Mad Magazine* is something I'd expect from you." He said it in such a way that Shelly couldn't possibly be offended.

"At least we agree on one thing."

He raised his thick brows in question.

"The French fries."

"Right." Lifting one from the package, he held it out for her.

Shelly leaned toward him and captured the fry in her mouth. The gesture was oddly intimate, and her smile faded as her gaze clashed with Slade's. It was happening again. That heart-pounding, room-fading-away, shallow-breathing syndrome. Obviously this . . . feeling . . . had something to do with the weather. Maybe she could blame it on the season of love and goodwill toward all mankind. Shelly, unfortunately, seemed to be overly infected with benevolence this Christmas. Experiencing the sensations she was, heaven only knows what would happen if she spied mistletoe.

Slade raked his hand through his well-groomed hair, mussing it. Quickly he diverted his gaze out the window. "It looks like it might be letting up a little."

"Yes, it does," she agreed without so much as looking out the window. The French fries seemed to demand her full attention.

"I suppose we should think about heading out."

"I suppose." A glance at her watch confirmed that it was well into the afternoon. "I'm sorry about your appointment."

Slade looked at her blankly for a moment. "Oh, that. I knew when I left that there was little likelihood that I'd be able to make it today. That's why I made arrangements to meet tomorrow morning."

"It's been an enjoyable break."

"Very," he agreed.

"Do you think we'll have any more problems?"

"We could, but there are enough businesses along the way that we don't need to worry about getting stranded."

"In other words, we could hit every fast-food spot between here and Seattle."

Slade responded with a soft chuckle. "Right."

"Well, in that case, bring on the French fries."

By the time they were back on the freeway, Shelly noted that the storm had indeed abated. But the radio issued a weather update that called for more snow. Slade groaned.

"You could always spend Christmas with me and Dad." Shelly broached the subject carefully. "We'd like to have you. Honest."

Slade tossed her a disbelieving glare. "You don't mean that?"

"Of course I do."

"But I'm a stranger."

"I've shared French fries with you. It's been a long time since I've been that intimate with a man. In fact, it would be best if you didn't mention it to my dad. He might be inclined to reach for his shotgun."

It took a minute for Slade to understand the implication. "A shotgun wedding?"

"I am getting on in years. Dad would like to see me married off and producing grandchildren. My brothers have been lax in that department." For the moment she'd forgotten about Margaret. When she remembered, Shelly felt her spirits rush out of her with all the force of a deflating balloon. "Don't worry," she was quick to add. "All you need to do is tell Dad about your fiancée and he'll let you off the hook." Somehow she managed to keep her voice cheerful.

"It's a good thing I didn't take a bite of your hamburger."

"Are you kidding? That would have put me directly into your last will and testament."

"I was afraid of that," he said, laughing good-naturedly.

Once again Shelly was reminded of how rich and deep the sound of Slade's laughter was. It had the most overwhelming effect on her. She discovered that, when he laughed, nothing could keep her spirits down.

Their progress was hampered by the swirling snow until their forward movement became little more than a crawl. Shelly didn't mind. They chatted, joked and sang along with the radio. She discovered that she enjoyed Slade's wit. Although a bit dry, under that gruff, serious exterior lay an interesting man with a warm but subtle sense of humor. Given any other set of circumstances, Shelly would have liked to get to know Slade Garner better.

"What'd you buy your dad for Christmas?"

The question came so unexpectedly that it took Shelly a moment to realize that he was speaking to her.

"Are you concerned that I wrapped up soup to go with the bread?"

Slade scowled, momentarily puzzled. "Ah, to go with the sourdough bread. No, I was just curious."

"First, I got him a box of his favorite chocolate-covered cherries."

"I should have known it'd be food."

"That's not all," she countered a bit testily. "We exchange the usual father-daughter gifts. You know. Things like stirrup irons, bridles and horse blankets. That's what Dad got me last Christmas."

Slade cleared his throat. "Just the usual items every father buys his daughter. What about this year?"

"Since I'm not around Sampson, I imagine he'll resort to the old standbys, like towels and sheets for my apartment." She was half hoping that, at the mention of her place in San Francisco, Slade would turn the conversation in that direction. He didn't, and she was hard-pressed to hide her disappointment.

"What about you?"

"Me?" His gaze flickered momentarily from the road.

"What did you buy your family?"

Slade gave her an uncomfortable look. "Well, actually, I didn't. It seemed simpler this year just to send them money."

"I see." Shelly knew that that was perfectly acceptable in some cases, but it sounded so cold and uncaring for a son to resort to a gift of money. Undoubtedly, once he and Margaret were married, they'd shop together for something more appropriate.

"I wish now that I hadn't. I think my parents would have enjoyed fresh sourdough bread and chocolate-covered cherries." He hesitated for an instant. "I'm not as confident about the stirrups and horse blankets, however."

As they neared Tacoma, Shelly was surprised at how heavy the traffic had gotten. The closer they came to Maple Valley, the more anxious she became.

"My exit isn't far," she told him, growing impatient. "Good grief, one would expect people to stay off the roads in weather like this."

"Exactly," Slade echoed her thoughts.

It wasn't until she heard the soft timbre of his chuckle that she realized he was teasing her. "You know what I mean."

He didn't answer as he edged the car ahead. Already the night was pitch-dark. Snow continued to fall with astonishing regularity. Shelly wondered when it would stop. She was concerned about Slade driving alone from Maple Valley to Seattle.

"Maybe it would be better if we found a place to stop and phoned my dad."

"Why?"

"That way he could come and pick me up and you wouldn't—"

"I agreed to deliver you to Maple Creek, and I intend to do exactly that."

"Maple Valley," she corrected.

"Wherever. A deal is a deal. Right?"

A rush of pleasure assaulted her vulnerable heart. Slade wasn't any more eager to put an end to their adventure than she was.

"It's the next exit," she informed him, giving him the directions to the ten-acre spread that lay on the outskirts of town. Taking out a pen and paper, she drew a detailed map for Slade so that he wouldn't get lost on the return trip to the freeway. Under the cover of night, there was little to distinguish one road from another, and he could easily become confused.

Sitting upright, Shelly excitedly pointed to her left. "Turn here."

Apparently in preparation for his departure to the airport, her father had shoveled the snow from the long driveway.

The headlights cut into the night, revealing the long, sprawling ranch house that had been Shelly's childhood home. A tall figure appeared at the window and almost immediately the front door burst open.

Slade had barely put the car into Park when Shelly threw open the door.

"Shortcake."

"Dad." Disregarding the snow and wind, she flew into his arms.

"You little... Why didn't you tell me you were coming by car?"

"We rented it." Remembering Slade, she looped an arm around her father's waist. "Dad, I'd like you to meet Slade Garner."

Don Griffin stepped forward and extended his

hand. "So you're Shelly's surprise. Welcome to our home. I'd say it was about time my daughter brought a young man home for her father to meet."

Chapter Four

Slade extended his hand to Shelly's father and grinned. "I believe you've got me confused with sourdough bread."

"Sourdough bread?"

"Dad, Slade and I met this morning on the plane." Self-conscious, Shelly's cheeks brightened in a pink flush.

"When it looked like the flight wasn't going to make it to Seattle, we rented the car," Slade explained further.

A curious glint darkened Don Griffin's deep blue eyes as he glanced briefly from his daughter to her friend and ran a hand through is thick thatch of dark hair. "It's a good thing you did. The last time I phoned the airport, I learned your plane still hadn't left Portland."

"Slade has an important meeting first thing tomorrow." Her eyes were telling Slade that she was ready to make the break. She could say goodbye and wish him every happiness. Their time together had been too short for any regrets.

"There's no need for us to stand out here in the cold discussing your itinerary," Don inserted and motioned toward the warm lights of the house.

Slade hesitated. "I should be getting into Seattle."

"Come in for a drink first," Don invited.

"Shelly?" Slade sought her approval. The unasked question in his eyes pinned her gaze.

"I wish you would." *Fool,* her mind cried out. It would be better to sever the relationship quickly, sharply and without delay before he had the opportunity to touch her tender heart. Her mind shouted fool, but her heart refused to listen.

"For that matter," Don continued, seemingly oblivious to the undercurrents between Slade and Shelly, "stay for dinner."

"I couldn't. Really." He made a show of glancing at his wristwatch.

"We insist," Shelly added. "After hauling this bread from here to kingdom come, the least I can offer you is a share of it."

To her astonishment Slade grinned, his dark eyes crinkling at the edges. The smile was both spontaneous and personal—a reminder of the joke between them. "All right," he agreed.

"That settles it, then." Don grinned and moved to the rear of the car while Slade extracted Shelly's suitcase and the huge sack.

"What's all this?"

"Presents."

"For me?"

"Well, who else would I be bringing gifts for?"

"A man. It's time you started thinking about a husband."

"Dad!" If her cheeks had been bright pink previously, now the color deepened into fire-engine red. In order to minimize further embarrassment, Shelly returned to the car and rescued the long loaves of sour-dough bread. Her father managed the huge "tuba case" full of gifts while Slade carried the one small carry-on bag.

The house contained all the warmth and welcome of home. Shelly paused in the open doorway, her gaze skimming over the crackling fireplace and the large array of family photos that decorated the mantel above the hearth. Ol' Dan, their seventeen-year-old Labrador, slept on the braided rug and did little more than raise his head when Don and Slade entered the house. But on seeing Shelly, the elderly dog slowly came to his feet and with some difficulty ambled to her side, tail wagging. Shelly set the bread aside and fell to her knees.

"How's my loyal, mangy mutt?" she asked, affectionately ruffling his ears and hugging him. "You keeping Dad company these days?"

"Yeah, but he's doing a poor job of it," Don complained loudly. "Ol' Dan still can't play a decent game of chess."

"Do you play?" Slade's gaze scanned the living room for a board.

"Forty years or more. What about you?"

"Now and again."

"Could I interest you in a match?"

Slade was already unbuttoning his overcoat. "I'd enjoy that, sir."

"Call me Don, everyone does."

"Right, Don."

Within a minute the chessboard was out and set up on a tray while the two men sat opposite each other on matching ottomans.

Seeing that the contest could last a long while, Shelly checked the prime rib roasting in the oven and added large potatoes, wrapping each in aluminum foil. The refrigerator contained a fresh green salad and Shelly's favorite cherry pie from the local bakery. There were also some carrots in the vegetable drawer; Shelly snatched a couple and put them in her pocket.

Grabbing her Levi jacket with its thick wool padding from the peg on the back porch and slipping into her cowboy boots, Shelly made her way out to the barn.

The scent of hay and horses greeted her, and Shelly paused, taking in the rich, earthy odors. "Howdy, Sampson." She spoke to her favorite horse first.

The sleek, black horse whinnied a welcome as Shelly approached the stall and accepted the proffered carrot without pause.

"Have you missed me, boy?"

Pokey, an Appaloosa mare, stuck her head out of her stall, seeking her treat. Laughing, Shelly pulled another carrot from her pocket. Midnight, her father's horse and Sampson's sire, stamped his foot, and Shelly made her way down to his stall.

After stroking his sleek neck, Shelly took out the grooming brushes and returned to Sampson. "I suppose Dad's letting you get fat and lazy now that I'm not around to work you." She glided the brush down the muscled flank in familiar fashion. "All right, I'll admit it. Living in San Francisco has made me fat and lazy as well. I haven't gained any weight, but I feel flabby. I suppose I could take up jogging, but it's foggy and rainy and—"

"Shelly?"

Slade stood just inside the barn, looking a bit uneasy. "Do you always carry on conversations with your horse?"

"Sure. I've talked out many a frustration with Sampson. Isn't that right, boy?"

Slade gave a startled blink when the horse answered with a loud snort and a toss of his head, as if agreeing with her.

"Come in and meet my favorite male," Shelly invited, opening the gate to the stall.

Hands buried deep in his pockets, Slade shook his head. "No, thanks."

"You don't like horses?"

"Not exactly."

Having lived all her life around animals, Shelly had trouble accepting his reticence. "Why not?"

"The last time I was this close to a horse was when I was ten and at summer camp."

"Sampson won't bite you."

"It's not his mouth I'm worried about."

"He's harmless."

"So is flying."

Surprised, Shelly dropped her hand from Sampson's hindquarters.

Slade strolled over to the stall, a grin curving up the edges of his mouth. "From the look on your face when we landed, one would assume that your will alone was holding up the plane."

"It was!"

Slade chuckled and tentatively reached out to rub Sampson's ebony forehead.

Shelly continued to groom the horse. "Is your chess match over already?"

"I should have warned your father. I was on the university chess team."

Now it was Shelly's turn to look amused. She paused, her hand in midstroke. "Did you wound Dad's ego?"

"I might have, but he's regrouping now. I came out to meet the horse you spoke of so fondly. I wanted to have a look before I headed for Seattle."

"Sampson's honored to make your acquaintance." *I am, too,* her heart echoed.

Slade took a step in retreat. "I guess I'll get back to the house. No doubt your dad's got the board set for a rematch."

"Be gentle with him," Shelly called out, trying to hide a saucy grin. Her father wasn't an amateur when it came to the game. He'd been a member of the local chess club for several years, and briefly Shelly wondered at his strategy. Donald Griffin seldom lost at any game.

An hour later Shelly stamped the snow from her boots and entered the house through the back door, which led into the kitchen. Shedding the thick coat, she hung it on the peg and went to check the roast and baked potatoes. Both were done to perfection, and she turned off the oven.

Seeing that her father and Slade were absorbed in their game, Shelly moved behind her father and slipped her arms around his neck, resting her chin on the top of his head.

"Dinner's ready," she murmured, not wanting to break his concentration.

"In a minute," Don grumbled.

Slade moved the bishop, leaving his hand on the piece for a couple of seconds. Seemingly pleased, he released the piece and relaxed. As though sensing her gaze on him, he lifted his eyes. Incredibly dark eyes locked with hers as they stared at each other for long, uninterrupted moments. Shelly felt her heart lurch as she basked in the warmth of his look. She wanted to hold on to this moment, forget San Francisco, Margaret, the snowstorm. It became paramount that she capture this magic with both hands and hold on to it forever.

"It's your move." Don's words cut into the stillness.

"Pardon?" Abruptly Slade dropped his eyes to the chessboard.

"It's your move," her father repeated.

"Of course." Slade studied the board and moved a pawn.

Don scowled. "I hadn't counted on your doing that."

"Hey, you two, didn't you hear me? Dinner's ready." Shelly was shocked at how normal and unaffected her voice sounded.

Slade got to his feet. "Shall we consider it a draw, then?"

"I guess we better, but I demand a rematch someday."

Shelly's throat constricted. There wouldn't be another day for her or Slade. They were two strangers who had briefly touched each other's lives. Ships passing in the night and all the other clichés she had never expected would happen to her. But somehow Shelly had the feeling that she would never be the same again. Surely she wouldn't be so swift to judge another man. Slade had taught her that, and she would always be grateful.

The three chatted easily during dinner, and Shelly learned things about Slade that she hadn't thought to ask. He was a salesman, as she'd suspected. He specialized in intricate software programs for computers and was meeting with a Seattle-based company, hoping to establish the first steps of a possible distribution agreement. It was little wonder that he'd considered this appointment so important. It was. And although he didn't mention it, Shelly was acutely aware that if this meeting was successful, Slade would be that much closer to achieving his financial and professional goals—and that much closer to marrying dull, dutiful Margaret.

Shelly was clearing the dishes from the table when Slade set his napkin aside and rose. "I don't remember when I've enjoyed a meal more, especially the sourdough bread."

"A man gets the feel of a kitchen sooner or later," Don said with a crusty chuckle. "It took me a whole year to learn how to turn on the oven."

"That's the truth," Shelly added, sharing a tender look with her father. "He thought it was easier to use the microwave. The problem was he couldn't quite get the hang of that, either. Everything came out the texture of beef jerky.''

"We survived," Don grumbled, affectionately looping an arm around Shelly's shoulder. The first eighteen months after her mother's death had been the most difficult for the family, but life goes on, and almost against their wills they'd adjusted.

Slade paused in the living room to stare out the window. "I can't ever remember it snowing this much in the Pacific Northwest."

"Rarely," Don agreed. "It's been three winters since we've had any snow at all. I'll admit this is a pleasant surprise."

"How long will it be before the snowplows are out?"

"Snowplow, you mean?" Don repeated with a gruff laugh. "King County is lucky if they have more than a handful. There isn't that much call for them." He walked to the picture window and held back the draperies with one hand. "You know, it might not be a bad idea if you stayed the night and left first thing in the morning."

Slade hesitated. "I don't know. If I miss this meeting, it'll mean having to wait over the Christmas holiday."

"You'll have a better chance of making it safely to Seattle in the morning. The condition of the roads tonight could be treacherous."

Slade slowly expelled his breath. "I have the distinct feeling you may be right. Without any streetlights Lord knows where I'd end up."

"I believe you'd be wise to delay your drive. Besides, that will give us time for another game of chess."

Slade's gaze swiveled to Shelly and softened. "Right," he concurred.

The two men were up until well past midnight, engrossed in one chess match after another. After watching a few of the games, Shelly decided to say good-night and go to bed.

She lay in her bed in the darkened room, dreading the approach of morning. In some ways it would have been easier if Slade had left immediately after dropping her off. And in other ways it was far better that he'd stayed.

Shelly fell asleep with the insidious hands of the clock ticking away the minutes to six o'clock when Slade would be leaving. There was nothing she could do to hold back time.

Without even being aware that she'd fallen asleep, Shelly was startled into wakefulness by the discordant drone of the alarm.

Tossing aside the covers, she automatically reached for her thick housecoat, which she'd left at her father's. Pausing only long enough to run a comb through her hair and brush her teeth, she rushed into the living room.

Slade was already dressed and holding a cup of coffee in his hands. "I guess it's time to say good-bye."

Chapter Five

Shelly ran a hand over her weary eyes and blinked. "You're right," she murmured, forcing a smile. "The time has come."

"Shelly—"

"Listen—"

Abruptly they each broke off whatever it was that they had planned to say.

"You first," Slade said and gestured toward her with his open hand.

Dropping her gaze, she shrugged one shoulder. "It's nothing really. I just wanted to wish you and Margaret every happiness."

His gaze softened and Shelly wondered if he knew what it had cost her to murmur those few words. She did wish Slade Garner happiness, but she was convinced that he wouldn't find it with a cold fish like Margaret. Forcefully she tossed her gaze across the room. For all her good intentions, she was doing it again—prejudging another. And she hadn't even met good ol' Margaret.

His eyes delved into hers. "Thank you."

"You wanted to say something," she prompted softly.

Slade hesitated. "Be happy, Shelly."

A knot formed in her throat as she nodded. He was telling her goodbye, really goodbye. He wouldn't see her again because it would be too dangerous for them both. Their lives were already plotted, their courses set. And whatever it was that they'd shared so briefly, it wasn't meant to be anything more than a passing fancy.

The front door opened and Don entered, brushing the snow from his pant legs. A burst of frigid air accompanied him and Shelly shivered.

"As far as I can see you shouldn't have a problem. We've got maybe seven to ten inches of snow, but there're plenty of tire tracks on the road. Just follow those."

Unable to listen anymore, Shelly moved into the kitchen and poured herself a cup of hot black coffee. Clasping the mug with both hands, she braced her hip against the counter and closed her eyes. Whatever was being said between Slade and her father had no meaning. She was safer in the kitchen where she wouldn't be forced to watch him walk out the door. The only sound that registered in her mind was the clicking noise of the front door opening and closing.

Slade had left. He was gone from the house. Gone from her life. Gone forever. Shelly refused to mope. He'd touched her and she should be glad. For a time she'd begun to wonder if there was something physically wrong with her because she couldn't respond to a man. Slade hadn't so much as kissed her, and she'd experienced a closeness to him that she hadn't felt with all the men she'd dated in San Francisco. Without even realizing it, Slade had granted her the priceless gift of expectancy. If he was capable of stirring her restless heart, then so would another.

Humming softly, Shelly set a skillet on the burner and laid thick slices of bacon across it. This was the day before Christmas, and it promised to be full. She couldn't be sad or filled with regrets when she was surrounded by everything she held dear.

The door opened again and Don called cheerfully. "Well, he's off."

"Good."

"He's an interesting man. I wouldn't mind having someone like him for a son-in-law." Her father entered the kitchen and reached for the coffeepot.

"He's engaged."

Don snickered and there was a hint of censure in his voice when he spoke. "That figures. The good men usually are snatched up early."

"We're about as different as any two people can be."

"That's not always bad, you know. Couples often complement each other that way. Your mother was the shy one, whereas I was far more outgoing. Our lives would have been havoc if we'd both had the same personalities."

Silently Shelly agreed, but to admit as much verbally would reveal more than she wished. "I suppose," she murmured softly and turned over the sizzling slices of bacon.

Shelly was sliding the eggs easily from the hot grease onto plates when there was a loud pounding on the front door.

Shelly's gaze clashed with that of her father's.

"Slade," they said simultaneously.

Her father rushed to answer the door, and a breathless Slade stumbled into the house. Shelly turned off the stove and hurried after him.

"Are you all right?" The tone of her voice was laced with concern. Her heart pounding, she checked him for any signs of injury.

"I'm fine. I'm just out of breath. That was quite a hike."

"How far'd you get?" Don wanted to know.

"A mile at the most. I was gathering speed to make it to the top of an incline when the wheels skidded on a patch of ice. The car, unfortunately, is in a ditch."

"What about the meeting?" Now that she'd determined that he was unscathed, Shelly's first concern was the appointment that Slade considered so important to him and his company.

"I don't know."

"Dad and I could take you into town," Shelly offered.

"No. If I couldn't make it, you won't be able to, either."

"But this meeting is vital."

"It's not important enough to risk your getting hurt."

"My truck has been acting up so I took it in for servicing," Don murmured thoughtfully. "But there's always the tractor."

"Dad! You'll be lucky if the old engine so much as coughs. You haven't used that antique in years." As far as Shelly knew, it was collecting dust in the back of the barn.

"It's worth a try," her father argued, looking to Slade. "At least we can pull your car out of the ditch."

"I'll contact the county road department and find out how long it'll be before the plows come this way," Shelly inserted. She didn't hold much hope for the tractor, but if she could convince the county how important it was that they clear the roads near their place, Slade might be able to make the meeting.

Two hours later, Shelly, dressed in dark cords and a thick cable-knit sweater the color of winter wheat, paced the living room carpet. Every few minutes she paused to glance out the large living room window for signs of either her father or Slade. Through some miracle they'd managed to fire up the tractor, but how much they could accomplish with the old machine was pure conjecture. If they were able to rescue Slade's car out of the ditch, then there was always the possibility of towing the car up the incline.

The sound of a car pulling into the driveway captured her attention, and Shelly rushed onto the front porch as Slade was easing the Camaro to a stop. He climbed out of the vehicle.

"I called the county. The road crew will try to make it out this way before nightfall," Shelly told him, rubbing her palms together to ward off the chill of the air. "I'm sorry, Slade, it's the best they could do."

"Don't worry." His gaze caressed her. "It's not your fault."

"But I can't help feeling that it is," she said, following him into the house. "I was the one who insisted you bring me here."

"Shelly." His hand cupped her shoulder. "Stop blaming yourself. I'll contact Bauer. He'll understand. It's possible he didn't make it to the office, either."

Granting him the privacy he needed to make his phone call, Shelly donned her coat and walked to the end of the driveway to see if she could locate her father. Only a couple of minutes passed before she saw him. Proudly he steered the tractor, his back and head held regally so that he resembled a benevolent king surveying all he owned.

Laughing, Shelly waved.

Don pulled to a stop alongside her. "What's so funny?"

"I can't believe you, sitting on top of a 1948 Harvester like you owned the world."

"Don't be silly, serf," Don teased.

"We've got a bit of a problem, you know." She realized that she shouldn't feel guilty about Slade, but she did.

"If you mean Slade, we talked about this unexpected delay. It might not be as bad as it looks. To his way of thinking, it's best not to appear overeager with this business anyway. A delay may be just the thing to get the other company thinking."

It would be just like Slade to say something like that, Shelly thought. "Maybe."

"At any rate, it won't do him any good to stew about it now. He's stuck with us until the snowplows clear the roads. No one's going to make it to the freeway unless they have a four-wheel drive. It's impossible out there.''

''But, Dad, I feel terrible.''

''Don't. If Slade doesn't seem overly concerned, then you shouldn't. Besides, I've got a job for you two.''

Shelly didn't like the sound of that. ''What?''

''We aren't going to be able to go out and buy a Christmas tree.''

Shelly hadn't thought of that. ''We'll survive without one.'' But Christmas wouldn't be the same.

''There's no need to. Not when we've got a good ten acres of fir and pine. I want Slade and you to go out and chop one down like we used to do in the good old days.''

It didn't take much to realize her father's game. He was looking for excuses to get Slade and her together.

''What's this, an extra Christmas present?'' she teased. From all the comments that Don had made about Slade, Shelly knew that her father thought highly of him.

''Nonsense. Being out in the cold would only irritate my rheumatism.''

''What rheumatism?''

''The one in my old bones.''

Shelly hesitated. ''What did Slade have to say about this?''

''He's agreeable.''

''He is?''

''Think about it, Shortcake. Slade is stuck here. He wants to make the best of the situation.''

It wasn't until they were back at the house and Slade had changed into her father's woolen clothes and heavy boots that Shelly believed he'd fallen so easily in with her father's scheme.

"You don't have to do this, you know," she told him on the way to the barn.

"Did you think I was going to let you traipse into the woods alone?"

"I could."

"No doubt, but there isn't any reason why you should when I'm here."

She brought out the old sled from a storage room in the rear of the barn, wiping away the thin layer of dust with her gloves.

Slade located a saw, and Shelly eyed him warily.

"What's wrong now?"

"The saw."

"What's the matter with it?" He tested the sharpness by carefully running his thumb over the jagged teeth and raised questioning eyes to her.

"Nothing. If we use that rusty old thing, we shouldn't have any trouble bringing home a good-sized rhododendron."

"I wasn't planning to mow down a California redwood."

"But I want something a bit larger than a poinsettia."

Slade paused and followed her outside the barn. "Are you always this difficult to get along with?"

Jerking the sled along behind her in the snow, Shelly shouted, "There's nothing wrong with me. It's you."

"Right," he growled.

Shelly realized that she was acting like a shrew, but her behavior was a defense mechanism against the attraction she felt for Slade. If he was irritated with her, it would be easier to hold back her feelings for him.

"If my presence is such an annoyance to you, I can walk into town."

"Don't be silly."

"She shouts at me about cutting down rhododendrons and I'm silly." He appeared to be speaking to the sky.

Plowing through the snow, Shelly refused to look back. Determined, she started up a small incline toward the woods. "I just want you to know I can do this on my own."

His hand on her shoulder halted her progress, paralyzing her. "Shelly, listen to me, would you?"

She hesitated, her gaze falling on the long line of trees ahead. "What now?"

"I like the prospect of finding a Christmas tree with you, but if you find my company so unpleasant, I'll go back to the house."

"That's not it," she murmured, feeling ridiculously like an adolescent. "I have fun with you."

"Then why are we arguing?"

Against her will she smiled. "I don't know," she admitted.

"Friends?" Slade offered her his gloved hand.

Shelly clasped it in her own. She nodded wordlessly at him.

"Now that we've got that out of the way, just how large of a tree were you thinking of?"

"Big."

"Obviously. But remember it's got to fit inside the house so that sixty-foot fir straight ahead is out."

"But the top six feet isn't," she teased.

Chuckling, Slade draped his arm across her shoulder. "Yes, it is."

They were still within sight of the house. "I don't want to cut down something obvious."

"How do you mean?"

"In years to come I don't want to look out the back window and see a hole in the landscape."

"Don't be ridiculous. You've got a whole forest back here."

"I want to go a bit deeper into the woods."

"Listen, Shortcake, I'm not Lewis and Clark."

Shelly paused. He'd used her father's affectionate term for her. "What'd you call me?"

"Shortcake. It fits."

"How's that?"

His gaze roamed over her, his eyes narrowing as he studied her full mouth. It took everything within Shelly not to moisten her lips. A tingling sensation attacked her stomach, and she lowered her gaze. The hesitation lasted no longer than a heartbeat.

His breath hissed through his teeth before he asked, "How about this tree?" His fingers gripped the top of a small fir that reached his waist.

Shelly couldn't keep from laughing. "It should be illegal to cut down anything that small."

"Do you have a better suggestion?"

"Yes."

"What?"

"That tree over there." She marched ahead, pointing out a seven-foot pine.

"You're being ridiculous. We wouldn't be able to get that one through the front door."

"Of course we'd need to trim it."

"Like in half," he mocked.

Shelly refused to be dissuaded. "Don't be a spoilsport."

"Forget it. This tree would be a nice compromise." He motioned toward another small tree that was only slightly bigger than the first one he'd chosen.

Without hesitating, Shelly reached down and packed a thick ball of snow. "I'm not willing to compromise my beliefs."

He turned to her, exasperation written all over his tight features. Shelly let him have it with the snowball. The accuracy of her toss astonished her, and she cried out with a mixture of surprise and delight when the snowball slammed against his chest, spraying snow in his face.

His reaction was so speedy that Shelly had no time to run. "Slade, I'm sorry," she said, taking a giant step backward. "I don't know what came over me. I didn't mean to hit you. Actually, I was aiming at that bush behind you. Honest."

For every step she retreated, he advanced, packing a snowball between his gloved hands.

"Slade, you wouldn't." She implored him with open arms.

"Yes, I would."

"No," she cried and turned, running for all she was worth. He overtook her almost immediately, grabbing her shoulder. Shelly stumbled and they both went crashing to the snow-covered ground.

Slade's thick torso pressed her deeper into the snow. "Are you all right?" he asked urgently, fear and concern evident in the tone of his voice as he tenderly pushed the hair from her face.

"Yes," she murmured, breathless. But her lack of air couldn't be attributed to the fall. Having Slade this close, his warm breath fanning her face, was responsible for that. Her breasts felt the urgent pressure of his chest, and even through the thick coats Shelly could feel the pounding rhythm of his heart echoing hers.

"Shelly." He ground out her name like a man driven to the brink of insanity. Slowly he slanted his mouth over hers, claiming her lips in a kiss that rocked the very core of her being. Their lips caressed while their tongues mated until they were both panting and nearly breathless.

Her arms locked around his neck, and she arched against him desperately, wanting to give him more and more.

"Shelly." His hands closed around her wrists, jerking them free of his nape. He sat up with his back to her. All she could see was the uneven rise and fall of his shoulders.

"Don't worry," she breathed out in a voice so weak that it trembled. "I won't tell Margaret."

Chapter Six

"That shouldn't have happened." Slade spoke at last.

"I suppose you want an apology," Shelly responded, standing and brushing the snow from her pants. In spite of her efforts to appear normal, her hands trembled and her pulse continued to hammer away madly. From the beginning she'd known that Slade's kiss would have this effect upon her, and she cursed her traitorous heart.

He swiveled, shocked that she would suggest such a thing. "I should be the one to apologize to you."

"Why? Because you kissed me?"

"I'm engaged."

"I know." Her voice rose several decibels. "What's in a kiss, anyway? It wasn't any big deal. Right?" *Liar*, her heart accused, continuing to beat erratically. It'd been the sweetest, most wonderful kiss of her life. One that would haunt her for a lifetime.

"It won't happen again," Slade said without looking at her. He held his body stiffly away from her. His facade slipped tightly into place, locking his expression right before her eyes. Shelly was reminded of the man she'd first seen on the plane—that polished, impeccable businessman who looked upon the world with undisguised indifference.

"As I said, it wasn't any big deal."

"Right," he answered. The light treatment that she gave his kiss didn't appear to please him. Standing, he stalked in the direction of the trees and stopped at the one he'd offered as a compromise earlier. Without soliciting her opinion, he began sawing away at its narrow base.

Within minutes the tree toppled, crashing to the ground and stirring up the snow. Shelly walked over, prepared to help him load the small fir onto the sled, but he wouldn't let her.

"I'll do it," he muttered gruffly.

Offended, she folded her arms and stepped back, feeling awkward and callow. She'd feel better if they could discuss the kiss openly and honestly.

"I knew it was going to happen." She'd been wanting him to kiss her all day.

"What?" he barked, heading in the direction of the house, tugging the sled and Christmas tree behind him.

"The kiss," she called after him. "And if I was honest, I'd also admit that I wanted it to happen. I was even hoping it would."

"If you don't mind, I'd rather not talk about it."

Slade was making her angrier every time he opened his mouth. "I said *if* I was being honest, but since neither of us is, then apparently you're right to suggest we drop the issue entirely."

Slade ignored her, taking giant steps so that she was forced into a clumsy jog behind him. The north wind whipped her scarf across her mouth, and Shelly tucked it more securely around her neck. She turned and took several steps backward so that the bitter wind buffeted her back instead of her face.

Unexpectedly her boot hit a small, protruding rock, and Shelly momentarily lost her balance. Flinging her arms out in an effort to catch herself, she went tumbling down the hill, somersaulting head over feet until she lay sprawled, spread-eagled, at the base of the slope.

Slade blistered the wind with expletives as he raced after her, falling to his knees at her side, his eyes clouded with emotion. "Do you have to make a game out of everything?"

She'd nearly killed herself, and he accused her of acrobatics in the snow. She struggled to give him a sassy comeback, but the wind had been knocked from her lungs and she discovered that she couldn't speak.

"Are you all right?" Slade looked concerned for the first time.

"I don't know," she whispered tightly. Getting the appropriate amount of oxygen to her lungs seemed to require all her energy.

"Don't move."

"I couldn't if I wanted to."

"Where does it hurt?"

"Where doesn't it would be a more fitting question." Belying her previous answer, she levered herself up with one elbow and wiggled her legs. "I do this now and then so I can appreciate how good it feels to breathe," she muttered sarcastically.

"I said don't move," Slade barked. "You could've seriously injured something."

"I did," she cried, "my pride." Slowly coming to her feet, she mockingly bowed before him and said, "Stay tuned for my next trick when I'll single-handedly leap tall buildings and alter the course of the mighty Columbia River."

"You're not funny."

"I was desperately trying to be."

"Here." He tucked a hand under her elbow. "Let me help you back to the house."

"This may come as a shock to you, but I'm perfectly capable of walking on my own."

"Nothing you do anymore could shock me."

"That sounds amazingly like a challenge."

Slade's indifference almost melted away as he stared down at her with warm, vulnerable eyes. "Trust me, it isn't." He claimed her hand, lacing his fingers with hers. "Come on, your father's probably getting worried."

Shelly sincerely doubted it. What Slade was really saying was that things would be safer for them back at the house. Temptation could more easily be kept at bay with someone else present.

He placed his hand at the base of her neck, and they continued their short sojourn across the snowy landscape.

The house looked amazingly still and dark as they approached. A whisper of smoke drifted into the clear sky from the chimney as though the fire had been allowed to die. Shelly had expected to hear Andy Williams crooning from the stereo and perhaps smell the lingering scent of freshly popped popcorn.

Instead, they were greeted by an empty, almost eerie silence.

While Slade leaned the tree against the side of the house, Shelly ventured inside. A note propped against the sugar bowl in the middle of the kitchen table commanded her attention. She walked into the room and picked it up.

Sick horse at the Adler's. Call if you need me.

Love,
Dad.

She swallowed tightly, clenching the paper in her hand as the back door shut.

"Dad's out on a call," she announced without turning around. "Would you like a cup of coffee? The pot's full, although it doesn't look too fresh. Dad must have put it on before he left. He knew how cold we'd be when we got back." She realized she was chattering and immediately stopped. Not waiting for his response, she reached for two mugs.

"Coffee sounds fine." Slade's voice was heavy with dread. The same dread that Shelly felt pressing against her heart. Her father was the buffer they needed and he was gone.

Shelly heard Slade drag out a kitchen chair, and she placed the mug in front of him. Her thick lashes fanned downward as she avoided his gaze.

Reluctantly she pulled out the chair opposite his and joined him at the table. "I suppose we should put up the tree."

Slade paused. "We might."

From all the enthusiasm he displayed, they could have been discussing income taxes. Shelly's heart ached. She was embarrassed at having made the suggestion. No doubt good ol' Margaret had hers flocked and decorated without ever involving Slade.

Her hands compressed around the mug, burning the sensitive skin of her palms.

"Well?" he prompted.

"I think I'll wait until Dad's back. We—every year since Mom died, we've done it together. It's a fun time." The walls of the kitchen seemed to be closing in on them. With every breath Shelly drew, she became more aware of the man sitting across from her. They'd tried to pretend, but the kiss had changed everything. The taste of him lingered on her lips, and unconsciously she ran her tongue over them, wanting to recapture that sensation before it disappeared forever.

Slade's eyes followed her movement, and he abruptly stood, marching across the kitchen to place his half-full mug in the sink.

"I'll tend the fire," he offered, hastily leaving the room.

"Thank you."

After emptying her own mug in the sink, Shelly joined him, standing in the archway between the kitchen and living room.

Slade placed a small log in the red coals, and instantly flames sizzled over the dry bark. Soon the fire crackled and hissed at the fresh supply of wood with ardent, hungry flames.

"I wonder what's happening with the road crew," Slade said.

"They could be here any time."

Together they moved toward the phone, each intent on collecting the needed information. In their eagerness they collided. Shelly felt the full impact of the unexpected contact with Slade. Her breath caught someplace between her lungs and her throat but not from any pain.

"Shelly." His arms went around her faster than a shooting star. "Did I hurt you?"

One hand was trapped against his broad chest while the other hung loosely at her side. "I'm fine," she managed, her voice as unsteady as his. Still, he didn't release her.

Savoring his nearness and warmth, Shelly closed her eyes and pressed her head to his chest, listening to the beat of his heart beneath her ear.

Slade went utterly still until his arms tightened around her, and he groaned her name.

Nothing that felt this wonderful and good could be wrong. Shelly knew that in her heart, but her head buzzed with a nagging warning. Even though her eyes were closed, she could see flashing red lights. Slade had held and kissed her only once and had instantly regretted it. He'd even refused to talk about it, closing himself off from her.

Yet the arguments melted away like snow in a spring thaw when she was in his arms. His lips moved to her hair, and he breathed in deeply as though to capture her scent.

"Shelly," he pleaded, his voice husky with emotion. "Tell me to stop."

The words wouldn't form. She knew that she should break away and save them both the agony of guilt. But she couldn't.

"I want you to hold me," she whispered. "Just hold me."

Automatically his arms anchored her against him, and his lips nuzzled her ear, shooting tingles of pleasure down her spine. From her ear he found her cheek, her hair. For an eternity he hesitated.

The phone jingled and they broke apart with a suddenness that rocked Shelly. Slade's hand on her shoulder steadied her. Brushing the hair from her face, she drew in a steadying breath.

"Hello." Her voice was barely above a whisper when she answered.

"Shelly? Are you all right? You don't sound like yourself."

"Oh, hi, Dad." She glanced up guiltily at Slade. His returning look was heavy with consternation. He brushed a hand through his own hair and walked to the picture window. "We got the tree."

"That's good." Don Griffin paused. "Are you sure everything's fine?"

"Of course I'm sure," she answered, somewhat defensively. "How are things with the Adlers?"

"Not good. I may be here a while. I'm sorry to be away from you, but Slade's there to keep you company."

"How . . . long will you be?"

"A couple of hours, three at the most. You and Slade will be all right, won't you?"

"Oh, sure."

But her father didn't sound any more convinced than Shelly felt.

Five minutes later Shelly replaced the receiver. The air in the room seemed to vibrate with Slade's presence. He turned around and held her gaze. "I've got to get to Seattle."

What he was really saying was that he had to get away from her. "I know," she told him in a tortured whisper. "But how?"

"How'd your dad get to that sick horse?"

"The Adler's neighbor, Ted Wilkens, has a four-wheel drive. I suppose he came for Dad."

"Would it be possible for him to take me into Seattle?"

Shelly hadn't thought of that. "I'm not sure. I don't think he'd mind. I'll call."

"It's Christmas Eve." Slade sounded hesitant.

"They're that kind of people," she said, reaching for the phone. Slade paced the small area in front of her while she talked to Connie Wilkens.

"Well?" Slade studied her expectantly as she hung up the phone.

"Ted's out helping someone else, but Connie thinks he'll be back before dark. She suggested that we head their way, and by the time we arrive, Ted should be home."

"You're sure he won't mind?"

"Positive. Ted and Connie are always helping others."

"Good people—like you and your dad," Slade murmured softly.

Shelly laced her fingers together in front of her. "Yes. We're neighbors, although they're a good four miles from here. And friends." She scooted down in front of Ol' Dan and petted him in long, soothing strokes. "I told Connie that we'd start out soon."

Slade's brow furrowed as her words sank in. "But how? The tractor?"

"I couldn't run that thing if my life depended on it."

"Me, either. Shelly, we can't trek that distance on foot."

"I wasn't thinking of walking."

"What other way is there?"

A smile grew on her soft features until it touched her eyes, which sparkled with mischief. "We can always take the horses."

Chapter Seven

"You have to be kidding!" Slade gave her a look of pure disbelief.

"No," Shelly insisted, swallowing a laugh. "It's the only possible way I know to get there. We can go up through the woods where the snow isn't as deep."

Rubbing a hand over his eyes, Slade stalked to the far side of the room, made an abrupt about-face and returned to his former position. "I don't know. You seem to view life as one big adventure after another. I'm not used to..."

"Pokey's as gentle as a lamb," she murmured coaxingly.

"Pokey?"

"Unless you'd rather ride Midnight."

"Good grief, no. Pokey sounds more my speed."

Doing her best to hold back a devilish grin, Shelly led the way into the kitchen.

"What are you doing now?"

"Making us a thermos of hot chocolate."

"Why?"

"I thought we'd stop and have a picnic along the way."

"You're doing it again," he murmured, but she noticed that an indulgent half smile lurked just behind his intense dark eyes. Slade was a man who needed a little fun in his life, and Shelly was determined to provide it for him. If she was only to touch his life briefly, then she wanted to bring laughter and sunshine with her. Margaret would have him forever. But these few hours were hers, and she was determined to make the most of them.

"It'll be fun," she declared enthusiastically.

"No doubt Custer said the same thing to his men," Slade grumbled, following her out to the barn.

"Cynic," Shelly teased, holding open the barn door.

Reluctantly he followed her inside.

"How do you feel about a lazy stroll in the snow, Pokey?" she asked as she approached the Appaloosa's stall, petting the horse's nose. "I know Sampson's ready anytime."

"Don't let her kid you, Pokey," Slade added from behind Shelly. "Good grief, now you've got me doing it."

"Doing what?"

"Talking to the animals."

"They often show human characteristics," Shelly defended both their actions. "It's only natural to express one's feelings to 'almost' humans."

"In which case we're in trouble. Pokey is going to have a lot to say about how I feel when I climb on her back."

"You'll be fine."

"Sure, but will Pokey?"

"You both will. Now stop worrying."

When Shelly brought out the riding tack, Slade walked around the small barn, hands buried deep in his pockets. He did what he could to help Shelly saddle the two horses. Mostly he moved around her awkwardly, looking doubtful and ambivalent.

When she'd finished, she led the horses out of the barn. Holding on to the reins, she motioned for Slade to mount first. "Will you need any help?" she asked. Slade looked so different from the staid executive she'd met in Portland that she had trouble remembering that this was the same man. The one facing her now was clearly out of his element and nothing like the unflappable man on the airplane.

"I don't think so," he said, reaching for the saddle and trying to follow Shelly's directions. Without much difficulty he swung his bulk onto Pokey's back. The horse barely stirred.

Looking pleased with himself, Slade smiled down at Shelly. "I suppose you told her to be gentle with me."

"I did," she teased in return. Double-checking the cinch, she asked, "Do you need me to adjust the stirrups or anything?"

"No." Slade shifted his weight slightly and accepted the reins she handed him. "I'm ready anytime you are."

Shelly mounted with an ease that spoke of years in the saddle. "It's going to be a rough ride until we get under the cover of the trees. Follow me."

"Anywhere."

Shelly was sure that she'd misunderstood him. "What did you say?" she asked, twisting around.

"Nothing." But he was grinning, and Shelly found him so devastatingly appealing that it demanded all her willpower to turn around and lead the way.

She took the path that led them through the woods. Gusts of swift wind blew the snow from the trees. The swirling flakes were nearly as bad as the storm had been. Even Pokey protested at having to be outside.

"Shelly," Slade said, edging the Appaloosa to Sampson's side. "This may not have been the most brilliant idea. Maybe we should head back."

"Nonsense."

"I don't want you catching cold on my account."

"I'm as snug as a bug in a rug."

"Liar," he purred softly.

"I want you to have something to remember me by." She realized she must sound like some lovesick romantic. He would be gone soon, and she must realize that she probably would never see him again.

"Like what? Frostbite?"

Shelly laughed. The musical sound of it was carried by the wind and seemed to echo in the trees around them. "How can you complain? This is wonderful. Riding along like this makes me want to sing."

Slade grumbled something unintelligible under his breath.

"What are you complaining about now?"

"Who says I'm complaining?"

Shelly grinned, her head bobbing slightly with the gentle sway of Sampson's gait. "I'm beginning to know you."

"All right, if you insist upon knowing. I happen to be humming. My enthusiasm for this venture doesn't compel me to burst into song. But I'm doing the best I can."

Holding this contented feeling to her breast, Shelly tried not to think about what would happen when they reached the Wilkens's. She was prepared to smile at him and bid him farewell. Freely she would send him out of her life. But it had been easier before she'd been in his arms and experienced the gentle persuasiveness of his kiss. So very much easier.

Together, their horses side by side, they ambled along, not speaking but singing Christmas songs one after the other until they were breathless and giddy. Their voices blended magically in two-part harmony. More than once they shared a lingering gaze. But Shelly felt her high spirits evaporating as they neared the landmark that pointed out the first half of their short journey.

"My backside is ready for a break," Slade announced unexpectedly.

"You aren't nearly as anxious to scoff at my picnic idea now, are you?" Shelly returned.

"Not when I'm discovering on what part of their anatomy cowboys get calluses." A grin slashed his sensuous mouth.

They paused in a small clearing, looping the horses' reins around the trunk of a nearby fir tree.

While Shelly took the hot chocolate and cookies from her saddlebags, Slade exercised his stiff legs, walking around as though he were on a pair of stilts.

"We'll have to share a cup," she announced, holding out the plastic top of the thermos to Slade. She stood between the two horses, munching on a large oatmeal cookie.

Slade lifted the cup to his lips and hesitated as their eyes met. He paused, slowly lowering the cup without breaking eye contact.

Shelly's breath came in shallow gasps. "Is something wrong?" she asked with difficulty.

"You're lovely."

"Sure." She forced a laugh. "My nose looks like a maraschino cherry and—"

"Don't joke, Shelly. I mean it." His voice was gruff, almost harsh.

"Then thank you."

He removed his glove and placed his warm hand on her cold face, cupping her cheek. The moment was tender and peaceful, and Shelly swallowed the surging emotion that clogged her throat. It would be the easiest thing in the world to walk into his arms, lose herself in his kiss and love him the way he deserved to be loved.

As if reading her thoughts, Sampson shifted, bumping Shelly's back so that she was delivered into Slade's arms. He dropped the hot chocolate and hauled her against him like a man reaching out a desperate hand in need.

"I told myself this wouldn't happen again," he whispered against her hair. "Every time I hold you, it becomes harder to let you go."

Shelly's heart gave a small leap of pleasure at his words. She didn't want him to let her go. Not ever. Everything felt right between them. Too right and too good.

How long he held her, Shelly didn't know. Far longer than was necessary and not nearly long enough.

Each second seemed elongated, sustaining her tender heart for the moment she must bid him farewell.

Not until they broke apart did Shelly notice that it was snowing again. Huge crystal-like flakes filled the sky with their icy purity.

"What should we do?" Slade asked, looking doubtful.

Her first instinct was to suggest that they return to the house, but she hesitated. Delaying the inevitable became more difficult every minute.

"We're going back," he said, answering his own question.

"Why?"

"I'm not leaving you and your father to deal with the horses. It's bad enough that I dragged you this far." Placing his foot in the stirrup, he reached for the saddle and mounted the Appaloosa. "Come on, before this snow gets any worse."

"But we can make it to the Wilkens's."

"Not now." He raised his eyes skyward and scowled. "It's already getting dark."

Grumbling, she tugged Sampson's reins free of the tree trunk and lifted her body onto his back with the agile grace of a ballerina.

The house was in sight when Slade spoke again. "After you call the Wilkens's, I need to contact Margaret. She's waiting for my phone call. I told her I'd call Christmas Eve."

Shelly's heart constricted at the mention of the other woman's name. Unless Shelly asked about his fiancée, Slade hadn't volunteered any information about Margaret. Now he freely thrust her between them.

"Naturally, I'll use my credit card."

He seemed to feel her lack of response was due to the expense. Shelly almost preferred to think that. "Naturally," she echoed.

"She's a good woman."

Shelly didn't know who he was trying to convince. "I don't think you'd love a woman who wasn't."

"I've known Margaret a lot of years."

"Of course you have." And he'd only known Shelly a few days. She understood what he was saying. It was almost as if he were apologizing because Margaret had prior claim to his loyalties and his heart. He needn't; she'd accepted that from the beginning.

When they left the cover of the woods, Shelly spoke, managing to keep her voice level and unemotional. "You use the phone first," she said, surprised that her voice could remain so even. "I'll take care of the horses so you can make your call in private."

"I won't talk long."

Shelly didn't want him to tell her that. "Don't cut the conversation short on my account."

He wiped his forearm across his brow. The movement brought her attention to the confusion in his eyes. "I won't."

At the barn Shelly dismounted slowly, lowering both booted feet to the ground. She avoided his gaze as she opened the barn doors and led the horses through. The wind followed her inside the dimly lit area. The cold nipped at her heels.

With a heavy heart she lifted the saddle from Pokey's back before she noticed Slade's dark form blocking the doorway. Her hands tightened around the smooth leather of the saddle. "Is there a problem?"

"No."

After leading Pokey to her stall, Shelly turned back to Slade only to find that he'd left.

Taking extra time with the horses, she delayed entering the house as long as possible. Removing the gloves from her hands one finger at a time, she walked in the back door to discover Slade sitting in the living room staring blindly into the roaring fire. She walked quickly to the phone and called the Wilkens's. Connie was glad to hear from her. After a full day driving neighbors around in the snow, Ted was exhausted. Shelly assured her friend that Slade had changed his mind anyway.

"I don't know about you," she called out cheerfully after hanging up the phone, "but I'm starved." The tip of her tongue burned with questions that pride refused to let her ask. Shelly possessed the usual female curiosity about Margaret and what Slade had said, if anything, about his current circumstances.

"How about popcorn with lots of melted butter?"

Slade joined her, a smile lurking at the edges of his full mouth. His eyes were laughing, revealing his thoughts. He really did have wonderful eyes and, for a moment, Shelly couldn't look away.

"I was thinking of something more like a triple-decker sandwich," Slade inserted.

"You know what your problem is, Garner?" It was obvious he didn't so she took it upon herself to tell him. "No imagination."

"Because I prefer something meatier than pop-corn?"

Shelly pretended not to hear him; her head was buried in the open refrigerator. Without comment she brought out a variety of fixings and placed them on the tabletop.

Peeling off a slice of deli ham, she tore it in two and gave Slade half. "How about a compromise?"

He looked dubious, sure she was about to suggest a popcorn sandwich. "I don't know..."

"How about if you bring in the tree while I fix us something to eat?"

"That's an offer I can't refuse."

Singing softly as she worked, Shelly concocted a meal neither of them was likely to forget. Sandwiches piled high with three different kinds of meat, sliced dill pickles and juicy green olives. In addition, she set out Christmas cookies and thick slices of fudge that her father had sitting around the kitchen.

Slade set the tree in the holder, dragged it through the front door and stood it in the corner. "The snow's stopped," he told her when she carried in their meal.

"That's encouraging. I was beginning to think we'd be forced to stay until the spring thaw." Shelly wouldn't have minded, and her smile was a mixture of chagrin and ruefulness.

Sitting Indian style in front of the fireplace, their backs resting against the sofa, they dug into the sand-wiches. But Shelly discovered that she had little ap-petite. Never had she been more aware of a man. They were so close that, when she lowered her sandwich to the plate, her upper arm brushed against his. But neither made any effort to move. The touch, although impersonal, was soothing. She paused, wishing to capture this moment of peacefulness.

"This has been a good day," Slade murmured, his gaze following hers as he stared out the living room window.

"It's certainly been crazy."

Slade's hand reached for hers, entwining their fingers. "I don't know when I've enjoyed one more." His dark gaze flickered over her and rested on her mouth. Abruptly he glanced away, his gaze moving to the piano at the far side of the room. "Do you play?"

Shelly sighed expressively. "A little. Dad claimed that my playing is what kept the mice out of the house."

A dark brow lifted with a touch of amusement. "That bad?"

"See for yourself." Rising, she walked to the piano, lifted the lid of the bench seat and extracted some Christmas music.

Pressing her fingers to the ivory keys, the discordant notes were enough to make her wince and cause Ol' Dan to lift his chin and cock his head curiously. He howled once.

"I told you I wasn't any good," she said with a dramatic sigh. Staring at the musical notes a second time, she squinted and sadly shook her head.

Slade joined her. Standing directly behind her, he laid his hands on her shoulders, leaning over to study the music.

"This may be the problem," she stated seriously. Dimples formed in her cheeks as she tried not to smile.

Turning the sheet music right side up, she leaned forward to study the notes a second time and tried again. This time the sweet melody flowed through the house.

Chuckling, Slade's hands compressed around her shoulders, and spontaneously he lowered his mouth to her cheek. "Have I told you how much fun you are?"

"No, but I'll accept that as a compliment."

"It was meant as one."

Shelly continued to play, hitting a wrong note every once in a while and going back to repeat the bar until she got it right. Soon Slade's rich voice blended with the melody. Shelly's soprano tones mixed smoothly with his, although her playing faltered now and again.

Neither of them heard the front door open. "Merry Christmas Eve," Don announced, looking exhausted. His pants were caked with mud and grit.

Shelly rested her hands above the keys. "Welcome home. How's the Adler's horse?"

Don wiped a weary hand over his face. "She'll make it."

"What about you?"

"Give me a half hour and I'll let you know."

"There's a sandwich in the kitchen if you're hungry."

"All I want right now is a hot bath." He paused to scratch Ol' Dan's ears. "Keep playing. You two sound good together."

"I thought we were scattering the mice to the barn," Slade teased.

Don scratched the side of his head with his index finger. "Say that again?"

"He's talking about my piano playing," Shelly reminded her father.

"Oh, that. No, by herself Shelly doesn't appear to have much talent. I don't suppose you play?" He directed the question to Slade.

"As a matter of fact, I do."

"You do?" Shelly was stunned. "Why didn't you say something earlier? Here." She slid off the bench. "Trade places."

Slade claimed her position and his large, masculine hands ran over the keys with a familiarity that caused Shelly's heart to flutter. His hands moved over the keys with deep reverence and love. Stroking, enticing the instrument until the crescendo of the music practically had the room swaying. Music, wrapped deep in emotion, so overwhelmingly breathtaking that Shelly felt tears gather in the corner of her eyes. Slade didn't play the piano; he made love to it.

When he'd finished, he rested his hands in his lap and slowly expelled his breath.

Shelly sank into the cushioned chair. "Why didn't you tell me you could play like that?"

A smile brightened his eyes. "You didn't ask."

Even Don was awestruck and, for the first time in years, at a complete loss for words.

"You could play professionally. You're magnificent." Shelly's soft voice cracked with the potency of her feelings.

"I briefly toyed with the idea at one time."

"But..."

"I play for enjoyment now." The light dimmed in his gaze, and the sharp edge of his words seemed to say that the decision hadn't come easy. And it certainly was not one he was willing to discuss, even with her.

"Will you play something else?" Don requested, not moving.

From his look Slade appeared to regret admitting that he played the piano. Music was his real love, and he'd abandoned it. Coming this close again was pure torture for him. "Another time, perhaps."

There wouldn't be another time for them. "Please," Shelly whispered, rising and standing behind him. She placed her hands on his shoulder in a silent plea.

Slade's hand covered hers as he looked into her imploring gaze. "All right, Shelly. For you."

For half an hour he played with such intensity that his shoulders sagged with exhaustion when he'd finished.

"God has given you a rare and priceless gift," Don said, his voice husky with appreciation. He glanced down at his mud-caked clothes. "Now, if you'll excuse me, I'll take a bath before I start attracting flies."

Shelly could find no words to express herself. As Don left the room, she moved to Slade's side, sitting on the bench beside him.

Lovingly her fingers traced the sculptured line of his jaw as the tears blurred her vision. The tightness in her chest made her breathing shallow and difficult.

Slade's hand stopped her. Lifting her fingers to his lips, he gently kissed the inside of her palm. Shelly bit her bottom lip to hold back all the emotion stored in her heart.

A lone tear escaped and trickled down her pale cheek. With his thumb Slade gently brushed it aside.

His finger felt cool against her heated skin. He bent down and found her mouth with his. Without speaking a word, Shelly realized that Slade was thanking her. With her he'd allowed his facade to crumble. He opened his heart and revealed the deep, sensitive man inside. He was free now, with nothing more to hide.

Wrapping her arms around him, she kissed him in return, telling him the only way she could how much she appreciated the gift.

"Merry Christmas, Shortcake," Don greeted on the tail end of a yawn.

Shelly stood in front of the picture window, her hands cupping her coffee mug. Her gaze rested on the sunrise as it blanketed the morning with the bright hues of another day. She tried to force a smile when she turned to her father, but it refused to come. She felt chilled and empty inside.

"Where's Slade?" Don asked.

"The snowplows came during the night," she whispered through the pain. "He's gone."

Chapter Eight

"Gone? Without saying goodbye?" A look of disbelief marred Don's smooth brow.

"He left a note." Shelly withdrew it from her pocket and handed it to her father. The message was no more than a few lines. He thanked them for their hospitality and wished Shelly and her father much happiness. He said goodbye. Without regrets. Without second thoughts. Without looking back.

Don's gaze lifted from the note and narrowed as he studied his daughter. "Are you okay?"

"I'm fine."

He slowly shook his head. "I've never seen you look at a man the way you looked at Slade. You really liked him, didn't you?"

I love him, her heart cried. "He's a wonderful man. I only hope Margaret and that computer firm realize their good fortune."

"They don't, you know," Don whispered, coming to her side. He slipped an arm over her shoulder and hugged her close. She offered him a feeble smile in return.

"He might come back."

Shelly knew differently. "No." He'd made his choice. His future had been charted and defined as precisely as a road map. Slade Garner was a man of character and strength. He wouldn't abandon Margaret and all that was important to him for a two-day acquaintance and a few stolen kisses. He'd shared his deepest desires and secrets with her, opened his heart and trusted her. Shelly couldn't have wished for more. But she did. She wanted Slade.

Christmas day passed in a blur. She flew back to San Francisco the following afternoon, still numb, still aching, but holding her head up high and proud.

Her tiny apartment in the Garden District, although colorful and cheerfully decorated, did little to boost her drooping spirits.

Setting her suitcase on the polished hardwood floor, she kicked off her shoes and reached for the phone.

"Hi, Dad." Taking the telephone with her, she sank into the overstuffed chair.

"How was the flight?"

"Without a hitch."

"Just the way you like them." Don chuckled, then grew serious. "I don't suppose—"

"No, Dad." Shelly knew what he was asking. Don seemed to feel that Slade would be in San Francisco waiting for her. Shelly knew better. Slade wouldn't want to think of her. Already he'd banished any thought of her to the furthest corner of his mind. Perhaps what they'd shared was an embarrassment to him now.

Shelly spoke to her father for a few minutes longer, but neither had much to say. When they'd finished, she sat with the telephone cradled in her lap, staring blindly at the wallpaper.

For her part, Shelly worked hard at putting her life back on an even keel. She went to work each day and did her utmost to forget the man who had touched her so profoundly.

Her one resolution for the New Year was simple: Find a man. For the first time since moving to San Francisco, Shelly was lonely. Oh, there were friends and plenty of invitations, but nothing to take away the ache in her soul.

Two days before the New Year, Shelly stepped off the bus and on impulse bought flowers from a vendor on the street corner. One of her shoes had caused a blister on her heel, and she removed the offending pump once inside her apartment building.

The elderly woman who lived across the hall opened her door as Shelly approached. "Good afternoon, Mrs. Lester," Shelly said, pulling a red carnation from the bouquet of flowers and handing it to her neighbor.

"Now, isn't that a coincidence." Mrs. Lester chuckled. "I've got flowers for you."

Shelly's heart went still.

"The delivery boy asked me to give them to you." She reached back inside, then handed Shelly a narrow white box. "Roses, I suspect."

"Roses?" Shelly felt the blood drain from her face. She couldn't get inside her apartment fast enough. Closing the door with her foot, she walked across the room and set the box on a table. Inside she discovered a dozen of the most perfect roses she'd ever imagined. Each bud was identical to the others, their color brilliant. They must have cost a fortune.

Although she went through the box twice, she found no card. It would only be conjecture to believe that Slade had sent them. Unlikely, really. He wouldn't be so cruel as to say goodbye only to invade her life again. Besides, he'd claimed roses were expensive. She couldn't argue with that. They were.

The thought had just formed when the doorbell rang, and a delivery boy handed her a second long narrow box, identical to the first.

"Sign here." He offered her his ballpoint pen.

Shelly scribbled her name across the bottom of the delivery order and carried the second box to the kitchen table. Again she'd received a gift of a dozen red roses, and again there was no card.

No sooner had she arranged the flowers in her one and only tall vase when the doorbell chimed a third time. It was a delivery boy from another flower shop with a dozen roses.

"Are you sure you have the right address?" she questioned.

"Shelly Griffin?" He read off her street and apartment number and raised expectant eyes to her.

"That's me," she conceded.

"Sign here."

Again Shelly penned her name. And for a third time there was no card.

Having no vase to arrange them in, she emptied her jar of dill pickles onto a plate, rinsed out the container and used that. These she carried into the living room.

Whoever was sending her the roses was either very rich or else extremely foolish, she thought.

Hands pressed against her hips, she surveyed the small apartment and couldn't decide if it resembled a flower shop or a funeral parlor.

When the doorbell chimed again, she sighed expressively. "Not again," she groaned aloud, turning the dead bolt and opening the door.

But instead of opening it to a delivery boy as she expected, Shelly came face-to-face with Slade. He was so tall, dark and so incredibly good-looking that her breath became trapped in her lungs.

"Slade."

"Hello, Shelly." His eyes delved into hers, smiling and warm. "Can I come in?"

"Oh, of course." Flustered, she stepped aside.

"Do you realize you only have on one shoe?"

She looked down at her nylon-covered foot. "I forgot. You see, they're new and I wore them for the first time today so when—" She stopped abruptly. "Why are you here?" she demanded. With her hands behind her back, she leaned against the closed front door desperately wanting to believe everything she dared not even think about.

"I've missed you."

She closed her eyes to the tenderness that lapped over her in gentle waves. Few words had ever been sweeter. "How did the meeting go?"

"Fine. Better than expected."

"That's nice." Her gaze studied him, still unsure.

"I got a hefty bonus for my part in it, but I may have offended a few friends."

"How's that?"

"They were hoping I'd accept a promotion."

"And you aren't?" This sounded like something Margaret would love.

"No, I resigned this afternoon."

"Resigned? What did...Margaret have to say about that?"

"Well—" he took a step toward her, stopping just short of her but close enough to reach out and touch her if he desired "—Margaret and I aren't exactly on speaking terms."

"Oh?" Her voice went incredibly weak.

"She didn't take kindly to some of my recent decisions."

I'll just bet, Shelly mused. "And what are those decisions...the most recent ones?"

"I decided to postpone the wedding."

Shelly couldn't fault his fiancée for being upset about that. "Well, I can't say that I blame her. When—when's the new date?"

"Never."

"Never?" Shelly swallowed tightly. "Why not?"

"Why?" He smiled. "Because Margaret doesn't walk around with one shoe missing. Or haul sourdough bread across the country or laugh or do any of the things that make life fun."

Speechless, Shelly stared at him, love shining from her eyes.

"Nor does she believe I'll ever make a decent living as a pianist," Slade continued. "Hell, I'm over thirty now. It could be too late."

"But...?"

"But—" he smiled and reached for her, bringing her into the loving circle of his arms "—I'm going to give it one hell of a try. I'm no prize, Shelly Griffin. I don't have a job, and I'm not even sure the conservatory will renew their offer, but for the first time in a lot of years, I've got a dream.''

"Oh, Slade," she whispered and pressed her forehead to his broad chest. "I would consider it the greatest honor of my life to be a part of that dream."

"You couldn't help but be," he whispered, lifting her mouth to his. "You're the one who gave it to me."

*   *   *   *   *